CW00867724

The Girl Who Found Her Smile

Written by Adekemi Adeniyan
Illustrated by Dolph Banza
Inked by Tony Bakatubia
Coloured by Gihoza Prince
Edited by Eliza Squibb

This book is dedicated to my family, friends, mentors and everyone at Dentalcare Foundation who enables me to be fulfilled in and to be the Executive Director of an organization that I'm honored to be a part of.

Thank you for letting me serve, for being a part of our amazing organization, and for showing up every day and helping more children turn their pain into beautiful smiles.

My name is Anita.
I like crunching candies with my teeth.
Candies are so sweet and yummy.

When I finish one, I ask my mum for more.
My mum says candies are not good for my young teeth.
She wants me to eat more fruits than candies.

Mum tells me to brush my teeth twice a day:
Every morning when I wake up
and every night before I go to bed.
Brushing doesn't hurt, but I hate it.
I stay in the bathroom for a while,
then I get out without brushing.
Mum doesn't even know.

This morning, I am excited!
We are going to take a school photo.
My school uniform is very clean.
I am going to stand up tall.
I will show my most beautiful smile
to make the photo happy.

7

OH NO!
What happened to my tooth?
It hurts and my canine is all green!
This is not good for the school photo.
I don't think I can smile.

"Students, 3,2,1 smiiile! Everyone, open your eyes wide and give your biggest smile!"
CLICK!
But the teacher doesn't like the smile.
Not everyone was giving their biggest smile, in fact, I can't smile at all.

"Let's do it again.
Anita, this time, I want you to smile.
Ready? 3, 2, 1, smiiile!"

9

"I am sorry, teacher. I can't smile."

10

My friends asked, "why can't you smile, Anita?"
As I opened my mouth to speak, "my canine is...", they all ran away!
They couldn't understand why my tooth was green and my gums were swollen.

"Mum, I feel so sad. Because of me, the school picture will not be full of smiles.
I've lost my smile. I can't be beautiful if my gums are swollen.
I won't have any friends if my canine remains green."

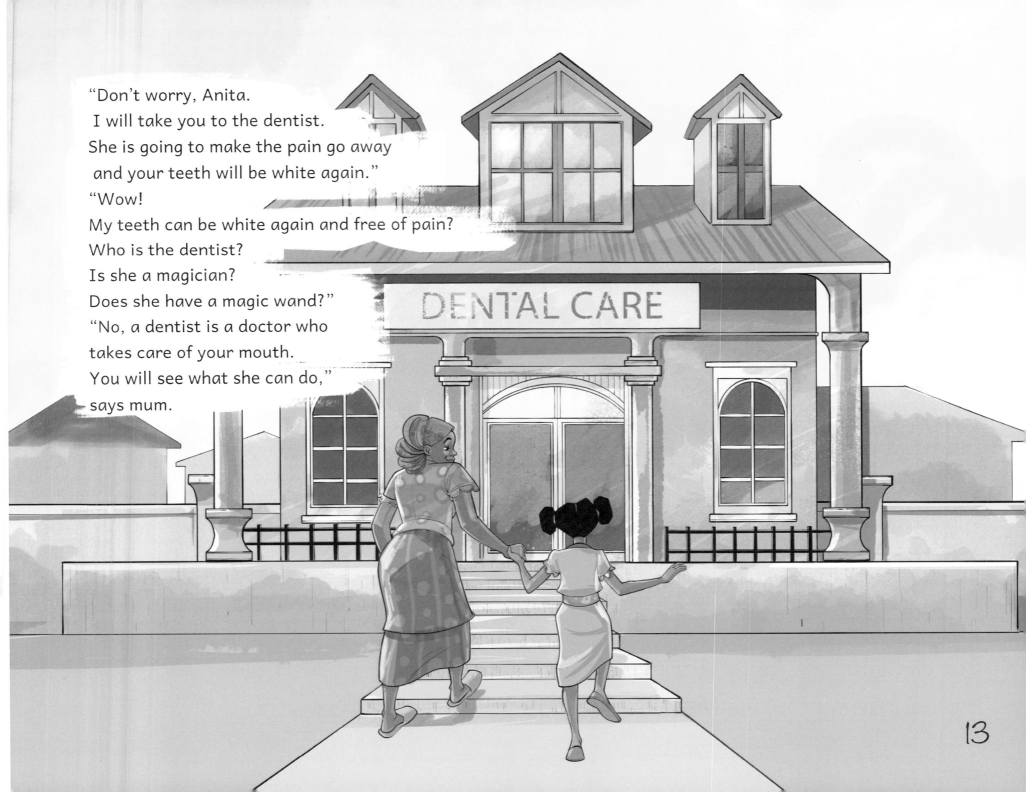

"Don't worry, Anita.
I will take you to the dentist.
She is going to make the pain go away
and your teeth will be white again."
"Wow!
My teeth can be white again and free of pain?
Who is the dentist?
Is she a magician?
Does she have a magic wand?"
"No, a dentist is a doctor who
takes care of your mouth.
You will see what she can do,"
says mum.

DENTAL CARE

13

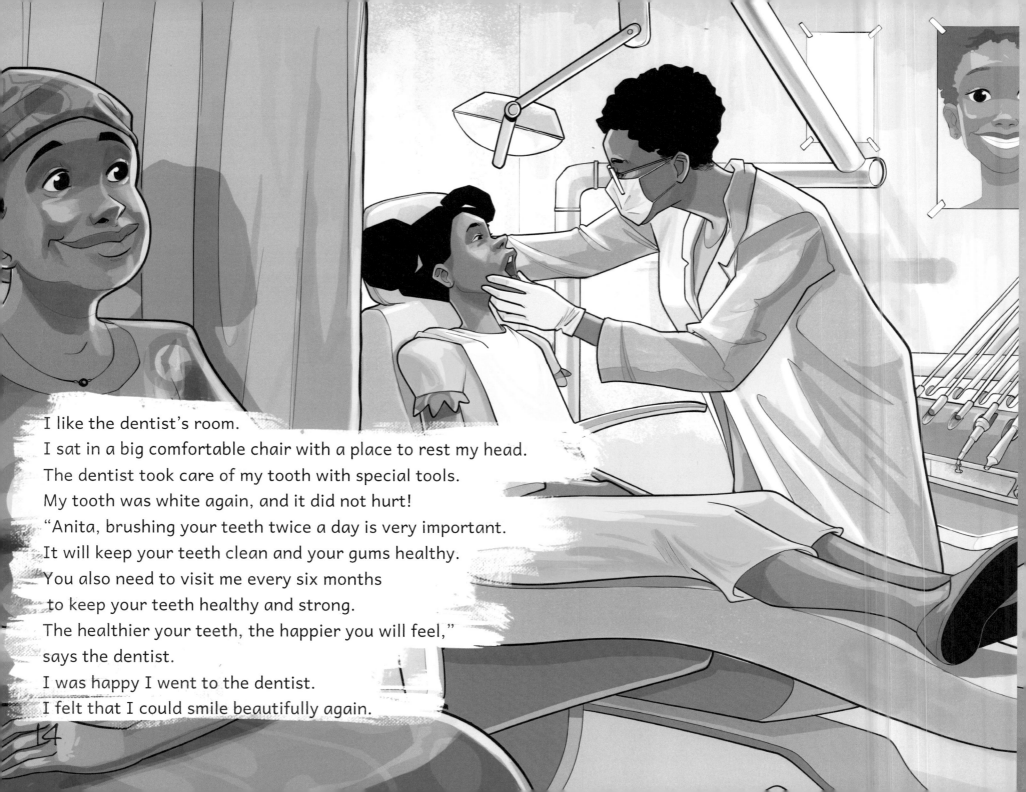

I like the dentist's room.

I sat in a big comfortable chair with a place to rest my head.

The dentist took care of my tooth with special tools.

My tooth was white again, and it did not hurt!

"Anita, brushing your teeth twice a day is very important.

It will keep your teeth clean and your gums healthy.

You also need to visit me every six months
 to keep your teeth healthy and strong.

The healthier your teeth, the happier you will feel,"
says the dentist.

I was happy I went to the dentist.

I felt that I could smile beautifully again.

14

This morning, I woke up very early to brush my teeth
like the dentist taught me.
Mum didn't even have to remind me!
I ate all my fruits at breakfast.
The dentist told me fruit is better for my teeth than candy.
I can't wait for the next school photo!
When my teacher says, "smile,"
I will stand up tall and show my beautiful, clean teeth.
It will be the best school picture ever!

The ABCs of Cavities

- A cavity is a hole that forms in a tooth when it is not taken care of. It can be painful and make your tooth eventually fall out.
- If you eat a lot of candies and sugary foods and don't brush regularly, you may have holes that form in your teeth.
- A dentist can treat holes in your teeth, so you have a clean mouth.

Cavities can be repaired, but you can avoid them also. Here's how:

- Eat healthy foods like vegetables, fruits, and milk.

- Rinse or brush after eating anything with sugar, especially sticky, sweet foods like candy.

- Brush your teeth two times a day, morning and night.

- See a dentist twice a year.

How to Brush

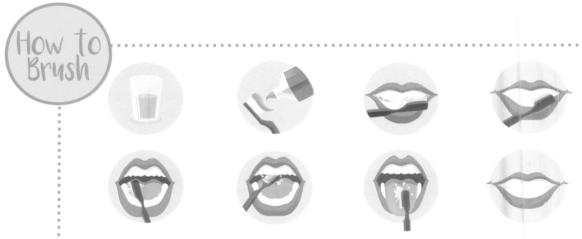

Step 1: Put your soft toothbrush at 45 degrees towards the gums.

Step 2: The toothbrush should be moved gently to clean the outer and inner part of the teeth and gums.

Step 3: The tip of the brush should be placed in an upright position to reach behind the front teeth on the top and bottom.

Step 4: Brush your tongue gently. After brushing, spit out the remaining toothpaste in your mouth but don't rinse out with water. Rinse your toothbrush and store in a clean place.

Healthy Teeth Goals

Do you want a healthy smile like Anita?
You can make a monthly pledge to keep your mouth clean and healthy.
Set your "Healthy Teeth Goals" today!

Here are some examples to start you on your path for a healthy mouth:

- I pledge to brush twice a day with no reminder
- I pledge to share Anita's story with a friend
- I pledge to visit the dentist twice a year for check up
- I pledge to eat more fruits and veggies than candies
- I pledge to use my tooth floss every day

Make up your own pledge and reward yourself with healthy,
clean teeth!

I pledge to

I pledge to

I pledge to

I pledge to

I pledge to

I pledge to

24

I pledge to

I pledge to

I pledge to

I pledge to

I pledge to